This Planner belongs to:

Every Heart Sings A Song
Incomplete Until Another Heart
Whispers Back

Plato

My Goals & Vision For My Wedding

My Goals & Vision For My Wedding

Wedding Planner ♡

WEDDING DATE & TIME:

TO DO LIST:

VENUE ADDRESS:

BUDGET:

OFFICIANT:

WEDDING PARTY:

NOTES & REMINDERS:

12 Months Before

- [ ] SET THE DATE
- [ ] SET YOUR BUDGET
- [ ] CHOOSE YOUR THEME
- [ ] ORGANIZE ENGAGEMENT PARTY
- [ ] RESEARCH VENUES
- [ ] BOOK A WEDDING PLANNER
- [ ] RESEARCH PHOTOGRAPHERS
- [ ] RESEARCH VIDEOGRAPHERS
- [ ] RESEARCH DJ'S/ENTERTAINMENT

- [ ] CONSIDER FLORISTS
- [ ] RESEARCH CATERERS
- [ ] DECIDE ON OFFICIANT
- [ ] CREATE INITIAL GUEST LIST
- [ ] CHOOSE WEDDING PARTY
- [ ] SHOP FOR WEDDING DRESS
- [ ] REGISTER WITH GIFT REGISTRY
- [ ] DISCUSS HONEYMOON IDEAS
- [ ] RESEARCH WEDDING RINGS

THINGS TO REMEMBER:

9 Months Before

♥

- [ ] FINALIZE GUEST LIST
- [ ] ORDER INVITATIONS
- [ ] PLAN YOUR RECEPTION
- [ ] BOOK PHOTOGRAPHER
- [ ] BOOK VIDEOGRAPHER
- [ ] BOOK FLORIST
- [ ] BOOK DJ/ENTERTAINMENT
- [ ] BOOK CATERER
- [ ] CHOOSE WEDDING CAKE

- [ ] CHOOSE WEDDING GOWN
- [ ] ORDER BRIDESMAIDS DRESSES
- [ ] RESERVE TUXEDOS
- [ ] ARRANGE TRANSPORTATION
- [ ] BOOK WEDDING VENUE
- [ ] BOOK RECEPTION VENUE
- [ ] PLAN HONEYMOON
- [ ] BOOK OFFICIANT
- [ ] BOOK ROOMS FOR GUESTS

THINGS TO REMEMBER:

6 Months Before

- ORDER THANK YOU NOTES
- REVIEW RECEPTION DETAILS
- MAKE APPT FOR DRESS FITTING
- CONFIRM BRIDEMAIDS DRESSES
- GET MARRIAGE LICENSE

- BOOK HAIR/MAKE UP STYLIST
- CONFIRM MUSIC SELECTIONS
- PLAN BRIDAL SHOWER
- PLAN REHEARSAL
- SHOP FOR WEDDING RINGS

THINGS TO REMEMBER:

3 Months Before

MAIL OUT INVITATIONS

MEET WITH OFFICIANT

BUY GIFTS FOR WEDDING PARTY

BOOK FINAL GOWN FITTING

BUY WEDDING BANDS

PLAN YOUR HAIR STYLE

PURCHASE SHOES/HEELS

CONFIRM PASSPORTS ARE VALID

FINALIZE RECEPTION MENU

PLAN REHEARSAL DINNER

CONFIRM ALL BOOKINGS

APPLY FOR MARRIAGE LICENSE

CONFIRM MUSIC SELECTIONS

DRAFT WEDDING VOWS

CHOOSE YOUR MC

ARRANGE AIRPORT TRANSFER

THINGS TO REMEMBER:

1 Month Before

- [ ] CONFIRM FINAL GUEST COUNT
- [ ] CONFIRM RECEPTION DETAILS
- [ ] ATTEND FINAL GOWN FITTING
- [ ] CONFIRM PHOTOGRAPHER
- [ ] WRAP WEDDING PARTY GIFTS
- [ ] CREATE PHOTOGRAPHY SHOT LIST

- [ ] REHEARSE WEDDING VOWS
- [ ] BOOK MANI-PEDI
- [ ] CONFIRM WITH FLORIST
- [ ] CONFIRM VIDEOGRAPHER
- [ ] PICK UP BRIDEMAIDS DRESSES
- [ ] CREATE WEDDING SCHEDULE

THINGS TO REMEMBER:

1 Week Before

- FINALIZE SEATING PLANS
- MAKE PAYMENTS TO VENDORS
- PACK FOR HONEYMOON
- CONFIRM HOTEL RESERVATIONS
- GIVE SCHEDULE TO PARTY

- DELIVER LICENSE TO OFFICIANT
- CONFIRM WITH BAKERY
- PICK UP WEDDING DRESS
- PICK UP TUXEDOS
- GIVE MUSIC LIST TO DJ

THINGS TO REMEMBER:

1 Week Before

	THINGS TO DO:	NOTES:
MONDAY		
TUESDAY		
WEDNESDAY		
THURSDAY		

REMINDERS & NOTES:

1 Week Before

	THINGS TO DO:	NOTES:
FRIDAY		
SATURDAY		
SUNDAY		

LEFT TO DO:

REMINDERS:

NOTES:

The Day Before

❤

- [ ] GET MANICURE/PEDICURE
- [ ] ATTEND REHEARSAL DINNER
- [ ] GET A GOOD NIGHT'S SLEEP!
- [ ] GIVE GIFTS TO WEDDING PARTY
- [ ] FINALIZE PACKING

TO DO LIST:

The Big Day

- GET HAIR & MAKE UP DONE
- HAVE A HEALTHY BREAKFAST
- ENJOY YOUR BIG DAY!
- MEET WITH BRIDESMAIDS
- GIVE RINGS TO BEST MAN

TO DO LIST:

Bridal ♥ Shows

Name	Location	Date

PRELIMINARY
Wedding Budget

	TOTAL COST:	DEPOSIT:	REMAINDER:
WEDDING VENUE			
RECEPTION VENUE			
FLORIST			
OFFICIANT			
CATERER			
WEDDING CAKE			
BRIDAL ATTIRE			
GROOM ATTIRE			
BRIDAL JEWELRY			
BRIDESMAID ATTIRE			
GROOMSMEN ATTIRE			
HAIR & MAKE UP			
PHOTOGRAPHER			
VIDEOGRAPHER			
DJ SERVICE/ENTERTAINMENT			
INVITATIONS			
TRANSPORTATION			
WEDDING PARTY GIFTS			
RENTALS			
HONEYMOON			

Wedding Party

MAID/MATRON OF HONOR:

PHONE: _____ DRESS SIZE: _____ SHOE SIZE: _____

EMAIL: _____

BRIDESMAID:

PHONE: _____ DRESS SIZE: _____ SHOE SIZE: _____

EMAIL: _____

BRIDESMAID

PHONE: _____ DRESS SIZE: _____ SHOE SIZE: _____

EMAIL: _____

BRIDESMAID

PHONE: _____ DRESS SIZE: _____ SHOE SIZE: _____

EMAIL: _____

BRIDESMAID

PHONE: _____ DRESS SIZE: _____ SHOE SIZE: _____

EMAIL: _____

BRIDE'S
Wedding Party

BRIDESMAID:

PHONE: _____   DRESS SIZE: _____   SHOE SIZE: _____

EMAIL: _____

BRIDESMAID

PHONE: _____   DRESS SIZE: _____   SHOE SIZE: _____

EMAIL: _____

BRIDESMAID

PHONE: _____   DRESS SIZE: _____   SHOE SIZE: _____

EMAIL: _____

BRIDESMAID

PHONE: _____   DRESS SIZE: _____   SHOE SIZE: _____

EMAIL: _____

BRIDESMAID:

PHONE: _____   DRESS SIZE: _____   SHOE SIZE: _____

EMAIL: _____

BRIDESMAID

PHONE: _____   DRESS SIZE: _____   SHOE SIZE: _____

EMAIL: _____

BRIDE'S

BRIDESMAID:

PHONE: _____ DRESS SIZE: _____ SHOE SIZE: _____

EMAIL: _____

BRIDESMAID:

PHONE: _____ DRESS SIZE: _____ SHOE SIZE: _____

EMAIL: _____

BRIDESMAID

PHONE: _____ DRESS SIZE: _____ SHOE SIZE: _____

EMAIL: _____

BRIDESMAID

PHONE: _____ DRESS SIZE: _____ SHOE SIZE: _____

EMAIL: _____

BRIDESMAID:

PHONE: _____ DRESS SIZE: _____ SHOE SIZE: _____

EMAIL: _____

BRIDESMAID

PHONE: _____ DRESS SIZE: _____ SHOE SIZE: _____

EMAIL: _____

GROOM'S Wedding Party

BEST MAN:

PHONE: _____   WAIST SIZE: _____   SHOE SIZE: _____

NECK SIZE: _____   SLEEVE SIZE: _____   JACKET SIZE: _____

EMAIL: _____

GROOMSMEN

PHONE: _____   WAIST SIZE: _____   SHOE SIZE: _____

NECK SIZE: _____   SLEEVE SIZE: _____   JACKET SIZE: _____

EMAIL: _____

GROOMSMEN

PHONE: _____   WAIST SIZE: _____   SHOE SIZE: _____

NECK SIZE: _____   SLEEVE SIZE: _____   JACKET SIZE: _____

EMAIL: _____

GROOMSMEN

PHONE: _____   WAIST SIZE: _____   SHOE SIZE: _____

NECK SIZE: _____   SLEEVE SIZE: _____   JACKET SIZE: _____

EMAIL: _____

GROOMSMEN

PHONE: _____   WAIST SIZE: _____   SHOE SIZE: _____

NECK SIZE: _____   SLEEVE SIZE: _____   JACKET SIZE: _____

EMAIL: _____

GROOM'S
Wedding Party

GROOMSMEN

PHONE: _____ WAIST SIZE: _____ SHOE SIZE: _____

NECK SIZE: _____ SLEEVE SIZE: _____ JACKET SIZE: _____

EMAIL: _____

GROOMSMEN

PHONE: _____ WAIST SIZE: _____ SHOE SIZE: _____

NECK SIZE: _____ SLEEVE SIZE: _____ JACKET SIZE: _____

EMAIL: _____

GROOMSMEN

PHONE: _____ WAIST SIZE: _____ SHOE SIZE: _____

NECK SIZE: _____ SLEEVE SIZE: _____ JACKET SIZE: _____

EMAIL: _____

GROOMSMEN

PHONE: _____ WAIST SIZE: _____ SHOE SIZE: _____

NECK SIZE: _____ SLEEVE SIZE: _____ JACKET SIZE: _____

EMAIL: _____

GROOMSMEN

PHONE: _____ WAIST SIZE: _____ SHOE SIZE: _____

NECK SIZE: _____ SLEEVE SIZE: _____ JACKET SIZE: _____

EMAIL: _____

GROOMSMEN

PHONE: _____ WAIST SIZE: _____ SHOE SIZE: _____

NECK SIZE: _____ SLEEVE SIZE: _____ JACKET SIZE: _____

EMAIL: _____

Bridal Gown

SHOP

Contact person .... Phone

Address

Website .... Email

Designer/Manufacturer

Style

Color/Fabric .... Train Length

Size .... Cost

First Fitting (date/time)

Second Fitting (date/time)

Final Fitting (date/time)

Pick-up (date/time)

NOTES

PLACE PICTURE HERE

Bridesmaids Attire ♡

SHOP

Contact person   Phone

Address

Website   Email

Designer/Manufacturer

Style

Color/Fabric

Cost

First Fitting (date/time)

Second Fitting (date/time)

Final Fitting (date/time)

Pick-up (date/time)

NOTES

PLACE PICTURE HERE

Bridesmaids Attire

SHOP

Contact person   Phone

Address

Website   Email

Designer/Manufacturer

Style

Color/Fabric

Cost

First Fitting (date/time)

Second Fitting (date/time)

Final Fitting (date/time)

Pick-up (date/time)

NOTES

PLACE PICTURE HERE

Grooms Attire

SHOP

Contact person   Phone

Address

Website   Email

Designer/Manufacturer

Style

Color/Fabric

Cost

First Fitting (date/time)

Second Fitting (date/time)

Final Fitting (date/time)

Pick-up (date/time)

NOTES

PLACE PICTURE HERE

Groomsmen Attire

SHOP

Contact person   Phone

Address

Website   Email

Designer/Manufacturer

Style

Color/Fabric

Cost

First Fitting (date/time)

Second Fitting (date/time)

Final Fitting (date/time)

Pick-up (date/time)

NOTES

PLACE PICTURE HERE

Flower Girl & Ring Bearer Attire

FLOWER GIRL

SHOP

Contact person	Phone
Address	
Website	Email
Designer/Manufacturer	
Style	
Color/Fabric	Size
Cost	
First Fitting (date/time)	
Final Fitting (date/time)	
Pick-up (date/time)	

RING BEARER

SHOP

Contact person	Phone
Address	
Website	Email
Designer/Manufacturer	
Style	
Color/Fabric	Size
Cost	
First Fitting (date/time)	
Final Fitting (date/time)	
Pick-up (date/time)	

Florist Planner

FLORIST:

PHONE: _____   COMPANY: _____

EMAIL: _____   ADDRESS: _____

FLORAL PACKAGE:

EST PRICE: _____

INCLUSIONS:	YES ✓	NO ✓	COST:
BRIDAL BOUQUET:			_____
THROW AWAY BOUQUET:			_____
CORSAGES:			_____
CEREMONY FLOWERS			_____
CENTERPIECES			_____
CAKE TOPPER			_____
BOUTONNIERE			_____

TOTAL COST:

Transportation

TO CEREMONY: PICK UP TIME: PICK UP LOCATION:

BRIDE: _____

GROOM: _____

BRIDE'S PARENTS: _____

GROOM'S PARENTS: _____

BRIDESMAIDS: _____

GROOMSMEN: _____

NOTES:

TO RECEPTION: PICK UP TIME: PICK UP LOCATION:

BRIDE & GROOM: _____

BRIDE'S PARENTS: _____

GROOM'S PARENTS: _____

BRIDESMAIDS: _____

GROOMSMEN: _____

Photographer

PHOTOGRAPHER:

PHONE: _____   COMPANY: _____

EMAIL: _____   ADDRESS: _____
_____

WEDDING PACKAGE OVERVIEW:

EST PRICE: _____

INCLUSIONS:	YES ✓	NO ✓	COST:
ENGAGEMENT SHOOT:			_____
PHOTO ALBUMS:			_____
FRAMES:			_____
PROOFS INCLUDED:			_____
NEGATIVES INCLUDED:			_____

TOTAL COST: _____

Videographer

VIDEOGRAPHER:

PHONE: _____   COMPANY: _____

EMAIL: _____   ADDRESS: _____
_____

WEDDING PACKAGE OVERVIEW:

EST PRICE: _____

INCLUSIONS:	YES ✓	NO ✓	COST:
DUPLICATES/COPIES:	☐	☐	_____
PHOTO MONTAGE:	☐	☐	_____
MUSIC ADDED:	☐	☐	_____
EDITING:	☐	☐	_____

TOTAL COST: _____

DJ and Entertainment

DJ/LIVE BAND/ENTERTAINMENT:

PHONE: _____   COMPANY: _____

EMAIL: _____   ADDRESS: _____

START TIME: _____   END TIME: _____

ENTERTAINMENT SERVICE OVERVIEW:

EST PRICE: _____

INCLUSIONS:	YES ✓	NO ✓	COST:
SOUND EQUIPMENT:	☐	☐	_____
LIGHTING:	☐	☐	_____
SPECIAL EFFECTS:	☐	☐	_____
GRATUITIES	☐	☐	_____

TOTAL COST: _____

Music Playlist

ARTIST	SONG	W R

Music Playlist

ARTIST	SONG	W R

Wedding Cake

PHONE: _____ COMPANY: _____

EMAIL: _____ ADDRESS: _____

WEDDING CAKE PACKAGE:

COST: _____ FREE TASTING: _____ DELIVERY FEE: _____

FLAVOR: _____

FILLING: _____

SIZE: _____

SHAPE: _____

COLOR: _____

EXTRAS: _____

TOTAL COST: _____

Caterer

CONTACT INFORMATION:

PHONE: _____   CONTACT NAME: _____

EMAIL: _____   ADDRESS: _____

MENU CHOICE #1:

MENU CHOICE #2:

	YES ✓	NO ✓	COST:
BAR INCLUDED:			_____
CORKAGE FEE:			_____
HORS D'OEURS:			_____
TAXES INCLUDED:			_____
GRATUITIES INCLUDED:			

Menu Planner

HORS D'OEUVRES

1st COURSE:

2nd COURSE:

3rd COURSE:

4th COURSE:

DESSERT:

Menu Planner

COFFEE/TEA:

FRUIT:

SWEETS TABLE:

WEDDING CAKE:

NOTES:

Rehearsal Dinner

REHEARSAL DINNER:

DATE: _____   LOCATION: _____

TIME: _____   NUMBER OF GUESTS: _____

NOTES:

CATERER: _____   ADDRESS: _____

PHONE: _____   EMAIL ADDRESS: _____

NOTES:

MENU: _____ ♥♥♥ _____

_____

_____

_____

_____

_____

_____

Favors

FAVORS

Company

Contact

Phone

Address

Website   Email

List favors and quantities

Total   Deposit Paid

                                 Date

Balance Due   Balance Due

                                 Date

Wedding Invitations

STORE/STATIONER

Contact

Phone

Address

Website   Email

♥ ♥ ♥

Style or Item Number

Paper Color

Lettering Style/Font

Ink Color

Quantity Ordered   Price

TEXT

Wedding Invitations
RSVP CARD

STORE/STATIONER

Contact

Phone

Address

Website   Email

♥ ♥ ♥

Style or Item Number

Paper Color

Lettering Style/Font

Ink Color

Quantity Ordered   Price

TEXT

Brainstorming

Brainstorming

Brainstorming

Brainstorming

Vision Board

Vision Board

Vision Board

Vision Board

Notes

Notes

Guest ♥ List

NAME:	ADDRESS:	# IN PARTY:	RSVP:

Guest ♥ List

NAME:	ADDRESS:	# IN PARTY:	RSVP:

NAME:	ADDRESS:	# IN PARTY:	RSVP:

Guest♥List

NAME:	ADDRESS:	# IN PARTY:	RSVP:

NAME:	ADDRESS:	# IN PARTY:	RSVP:

Guest ♥ List

NAME:	ADDRESS:	# IN PARTY:	RSVP:

NAME:	ADDRESS:	# IN PARTY:	RSVP:

Guest ♥ List

NAME:	ADDRESS:	# IN PARTY:	RSVP:

NAME:	ADDRESS:	# IN PARTY:	RSVP:

Guest ♥ List

NAME:	ADDRESS:	# IN PARTY:	RSVP:

Seating Planner

Table #

Table #

Seating Planner

Table #

Table #

Seating Planner

Table #

Table #

Seating Planner

Table #

Table #

Seating Planner

Table #

Table #

Seating Planner

Table #

Table #

Seating Planner

Table #

Table #

Seating Planner

Table #

Table #

Seating Planner

Table #

Table #

Seating Planner

Table #

Table #

Miscellaneous

Miscellaneous

Miscellaneous

Miscellaneous

Vendor Contact and Payment

Type	Name	Phone	Contract Date	Deposit	Balance Due	Due Date	Paid
Alterations/Seamstress							
Bridal Salon							
Bakery/Cakes							
Bartending Services							
Caterer							
Centerpieces							
Ceremony Musicians							
Ceremony Site							
Consultant/Planner							
Decorations							
Equipment Rentals							
Favors							
Florist							
Gift Table Attendant							
Gift Suppliers							
Officiant							
Photographer							
Reception Site							
Reception Musicians							
Reception							
Rehearsal Dinner							
Tuxedo Rental							
Transportation							
Travel Agent							
Videographer							
Other							

Detailed Budget

BRIDE	BUDGET	ACTUAL	COMMENTS
Bridal Gown			
Headpiece/Veil			
Jewelry			
Undergarments			
Stockings			
Shoes			
Alterations			
Garter			
Other			

BRIDESMAIDS	BUDGET	ACTUAL	COMMENTS
Bridesmaids' Dresses			
Headpiece			
Jewelry			
Shoes			
Alterations			
Other			

GROOM	BUDGET	ACTUAL	COMMENTS
Formal Wear Rental			
Shoes			
Other			

GROOMSMEN	BUDGET	ACTUAL	COMMENTS
Formal Wear Rental			
Shoes			
Other			

Detailed Budget

FLOWER GIRL	BUDGET	ACTUAL	COMMENTS
Dress			
Other			

RING BEARER	BUDGET	ACTUAL	COMMENTS
General Attire			
Other			

Subtotal #1_____

Working Budget ~ Misc.

BEAUTY	BUDGET	ACTUAL	COMMENTS
Hair/Make-up Artist			
Manicures			
Pedicures			
Spa Services			
Massage			
Other			

Subtotal #2_____

CAKES/BAKERS	BUDGET	ACTUAL	COMMENTS
Wedding Cake			
Cake Delivery/Set-up			

Detailed Budget

Cake Topper			
Cake Knife			
Sheet Cake			
Other			

Subtotal #3_____

CEREMONY/RECEPTION	BUDGET	ACTUAL	COMMENTS
Site Fee			
Ring Bearer Pillow			
Chairs			
Archway			
Guest Book/ Pens			
Pupus/Hors D'Oeuvres			
Main Meal/Caterer			
Beverages			
Bartending			
Bar Set-up Fee			
Corkage Fee			
Pouring Service			
Gratuity			
Parking Fees			
Other			

Subtotal #4_____

Detailed Budget

CONSULTANT/PLANNER	BUDGET	ACTUAL	COMMENTS
Consultant Fee			
Other			

Subtotal #5_____

ENTERTAINMENT	BUDGET	ACTUAL	COMMENTS
Ceremony Music			
Pre-Reception Music			
Reception Music			
DJ			
Emcee			
Sound System			
Other			

Subtotal #6_____

EQUIPMENT RENTAL	BUDGET	ACTUAL	COMMENTS
Tent/Canopy			
Tables			
Chairs			
Lighting			
Set-up/Breakdown			
Delivery			
Dance Floor			
Linens			

Detailed Budget

Beverage Items			
Serviceware			
Tableware			
Other			
Other			
Other			

Subtotal #7_____

FLOWERS & DECORATIONS	BUDGET	ACTUAL	COMMENTS
Ceremony Flowers			
Reception Flowers			
Centerpieces			
Favors			
Gift Table			
Flower Girl Basket			
Delivery/Set-up (Florist)			
Delivery/Set-up (Centerpieces/Favors)			
Balloons			
Candles			
Other			

Subtotal #8_____

Detailed Budget

INVITATIONS/STATIONERY	BUDGET	ACTUAL	COMMENTS
Bridal Shower			
Rehearsal Dinner& Brunch			
Welcome Wedding Signs			
Wedding Signs			
Envelopes&Address Labels			
Wedding Invitations			
Details Cards			
Rsvp Cards			
Thank You Cards			
Wedding Programs			
Wedding Menus			
Table Numbers			
Place Cards			
Postage			
Calligrapher			
Paper Napkins			
Matchbooks			
Wedding Certificate			
Other			

Subtotal #9_____

Detailed Budget

TRANSPORTATION	BUDGET	ACTUAL	COMMENTS
Limousine			
Tip			
Other			
Other			

Subtotal #10 _____

OFFICIANT	BUDGET	ACTUAL	COMMENTS
Officiant Service			
Gratuity			
Other			
Other			

Subtotal #11 _____

PHOTOGRAPHER	BUDGET	ACTUAL	COMMENTS
Engagement			
Announcement Photo			
Formal Bride Portrait			
Wedding Package			
Negatives			
Additional Prints			
Travel Fee			
Enlargements			
Touch-ups |Chrome Work			
Digital CD | USB			
Other			

Subtotal #12 _____

Detailed Budget

VIDEOGRAPHER	BUDGET	ACTUAL	COMMENTS
Wedding Day Video			
Extra Tapes			
Photo Montage			
Other			

Subtotal #13_____

SPECIALTY PRODUCTS	BUDGET	ACTUAL	COMMENTS
Bride's Gift			
Webpage			
Groom's Gift			
Bridesmaids' Gifts			
Groomsmen's Gifts			
Rehearsal Dinner			
Marriage License			
Bridal Gown Preservation			
Name Change Fees			
Honeymoon			
Crane/Tsurus Design			
Other			

Subtotal #14_____

Detailed Budget

HONEYMOON	BUDGET	ACTUAL	COMMENTS
Airline Tickets			
Car Rental			
Cruise Tickets			
Hotel			
Meals			
Entertainment			
Shopping			
Travel Insurance			
Taxes/Surcharges			
Tips			
Passport Fees			
Other			
Other			

MISCELLANEOUS	BUDGET	ACTUAL	COMMENTS

Subtotal #16 _____

Grand Total _____

Notes